Gail and Kait

by Liza Charlesworth

ISBN: 978-1-338-84444-3

Art Director: Tannaz Fassihi; Designer: Cynthia Ng; Illustrated by Michael Robertson
Copyright © Liza Charlesworth. All rights reserved. Published by Scholastic Inc.

3 4 5 6 68 26 25 24

Printed in Jiaxing, China. First printing, June 2022.

■ SCHOLASTIC

Gail did not like rain.
"Rain is a pain," said Gail.
"I will wait for sun."

Wait, wait, wait.
Rain, rain, rain.

Gail's pal Kait DID like rain.
"Time to get wet!" said Kait.
"OK," said Gail.
"But rain is a pain."

"It is fun to sail a boat!"
said Kait.
"Yes, it is," said Gail.
"But rain is a pain."

5

"It is fun to hop in a pail!"
said Kait.
"Yes, it is," said Gail.
"But rain is a pain."

6

"It is fun to sit on a log!"
said Kait.
"Yes, it is," said Gail.
"But rain is a pain."

7

"I see a snail!" said Kait.
Rain, rain, rain.

8

"I see a quail!" said Kait.
Rain, rain, rain.

"I see a pup.
It has a wet tail!" said Kait.
Rain, rain, rain.

Then...
NO rain, rain, rain.
"I see a rainbow!" said Kait.

11

"I see sun!" said Kait.
Sun, sun, sun.
But Gail is sad.

12

"Rain is not a pain," said Gail.
"It is fun, fun, fun!
I will wait for rain."

13

Read & Review

Invite your learner to point to each *ai* word and read it aloud.

tail

rain

wait

Kait

quail

Gail
sail
rainbow
pain
pail
snail

15

Fun Fill-Ins

Read the sentences aloud, inviting your learner to complete them using the *ai* words in the box.

> Kait pail pain tail rain

1. This story is about Gail and her pal,

   _____.

2. Gail says, "Rain is a _____."

3. Kait and Gail hop in a _____.

4. They see a pup with a wet _____.

5. At the end, Gail learns
   to like _____.